PIGS

Adult Coloring Book For Pig Lovers

Copyright © 2020 by Lasting Happiness
ISBN: 978-1-989842-16-4

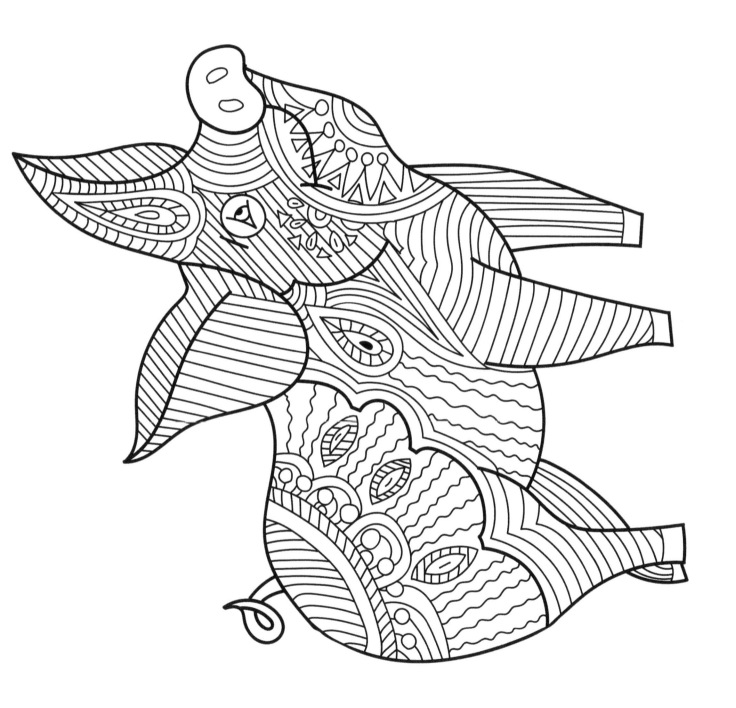

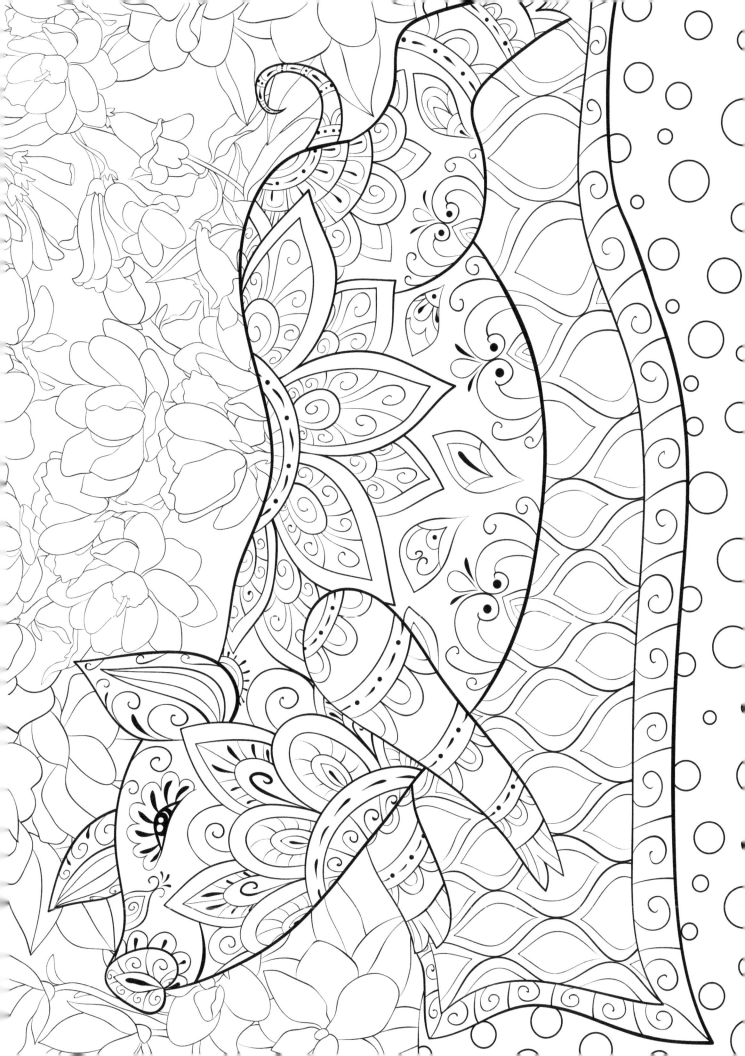

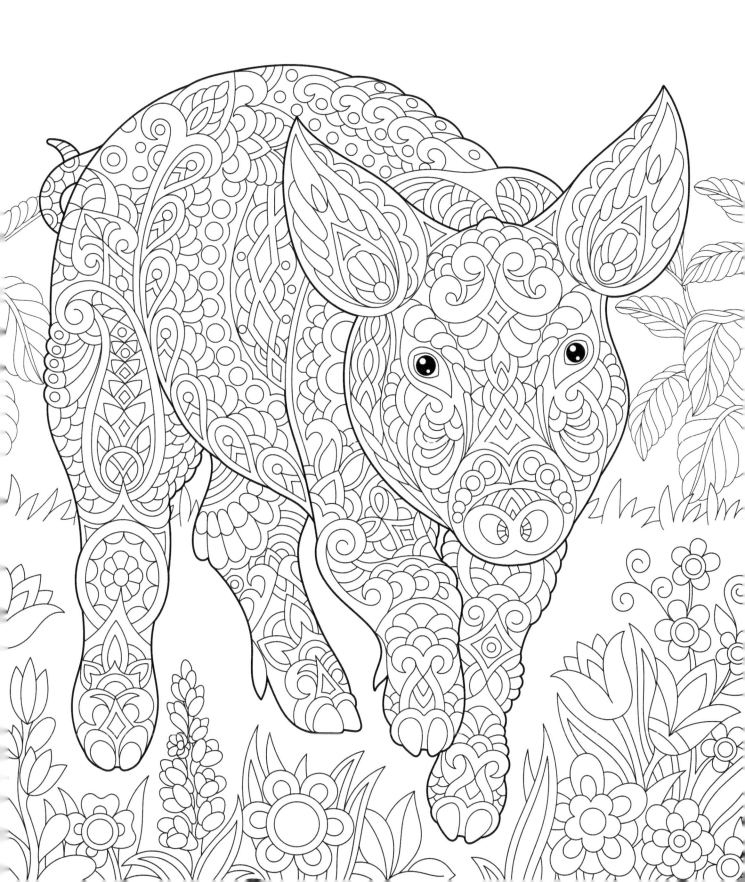

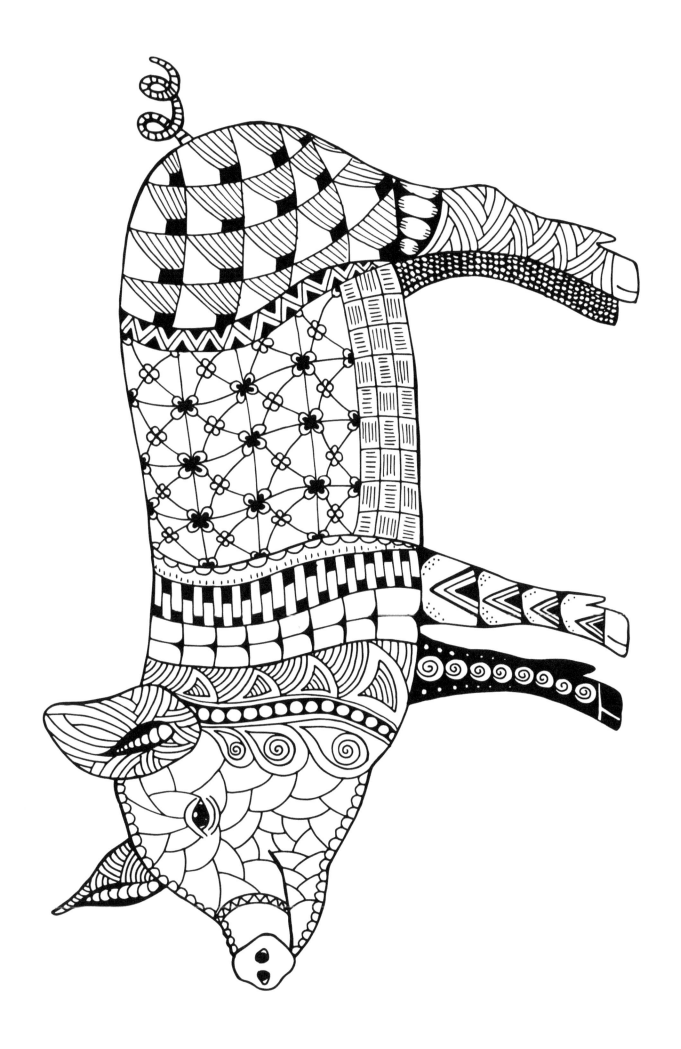

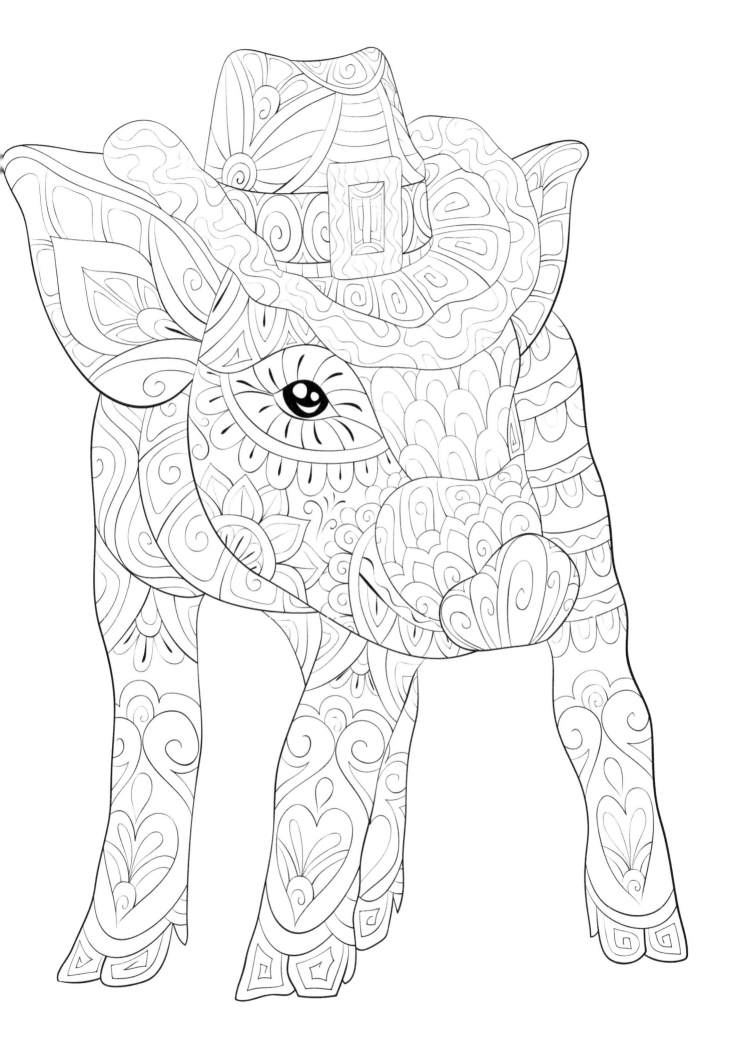

CPSIA information can be obtained
at www.ICGtesting.com
Printed in the USA
BVHW012008020222
627940BV00003B/26